Ladybird Readers

Too Much Porridge!
Activity Book

Based on the
Masha and the Bear TV series

Written by Catrin Morris
Song lyrics on page 16 by Wardour Studios

 Singing *   Reading   Speaking   Critical thinking

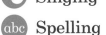 Spelling   Writing   Listening *

*To complete these activities, listen to tracks 2, 3, and 4 of the Reader audio download available at **www.ladybirdeducation.co.uk**

Look and read. Circle the correct words.

1

a jam

b oats

c porridge *(circled)*

2

a bowl

b game

c pot

3

a coffee

b milk

c water

4

a kitchen

b living room

c outside

2 Look at the pictures.
Write the correct words on the lines.

| mouth | ears | eyes | feet | nose | teeth |

1

.... mouth

2

....

3

....

4

....

5

....

6

....

1

Whose eyes are they?

They're Hedgehog's eyes.

2

Whose nose is it?

It's . . .

3

Whose feet are they?

They're . . .

4

Whose ears are they?

They're . . .

5

Whose mouth is it?

It's . . .

4 Look at the pictures.
Put a ✓ in the correct boxes. (abc)

1

a Hair ☐
b Hare ✓

2

a Bare ☐
b Bear ☐

3

a Hedgehog ☐
b Hegehog ☐

4

a Squirrel ☐
b Squirel ☐

5

a Woolfs ☐
b Wolves ☐

6

a porridge ☐
b porrige ☐

5 Do the crossword.

Down

1 You can eat from a . . .

2 A . . . is a big brown animal.

5 You make porridge from . . .

6 A . . . is an animal that lives in a tree.

Across

3 . . . is made with oats and milk.

4 Masha gave some porridge to Hedgehog, Squirrel, and the . . ., too.

7 You can cook in a . . .

6 Look at the pictures. Complete the sentences using the words in the box. 📖 ✏️

nice	big	happy	hot	hungry	new	old

1

It was a ....nice........, quiet day.

2

"Bear, we're ....," said Masha. "What can we eat?"

3

Bear was not .... He wanted to play his game.

4

"Yuck! I don't like Bear's ....
porridge," she said. "Let's cook some
.... porridge!"

5

Masha put some .... water in
a very .... pot.

It was a nice, quiet day.
Bear was in his living room.

He wanted to play a game.

Then, Masha and Hare came to Bear's house.

"Bear, we're hungry," said Masha. "What can we eat?"

6

7

1 Bear was in his living room. ....b........

2 It was a nice, quiet day. ....

3 Then, Masha and Hare came to Bear's house. ....

4 He wanted to play a game. ....

5 "What can we eat?" ....

6 "Bear, we're hungry," said Masha. ....

*To complete this activity, listen to track 2 of the Reader audio download available at www.ladybirdeducation.co.uk

8 **Look and read. Choose the correct words, and write them on the lines.** 📖 ✏️ ❓

Bear   bowl   Hedgehog

jam   porridge   pot

1 They are animals.

Bear, Hedgehog

2 You can eat these.

3 You put food in these.

9 Write *What*, *When*, *Where*, *Why*, or *Who*.

1 ....When.... did Masha and Hare go to Bear's house?
They went on a nice, quiet day.

2 .... did they go there?
They went because they were hungry.

3 .... made the porridge?
Masha made the porridge.

4 .... color was the porridge?
It was pink.

5 .... did Masha put all the porridge?
She put it in every pot and bowl in the house.

10 Look, match, and write the words.

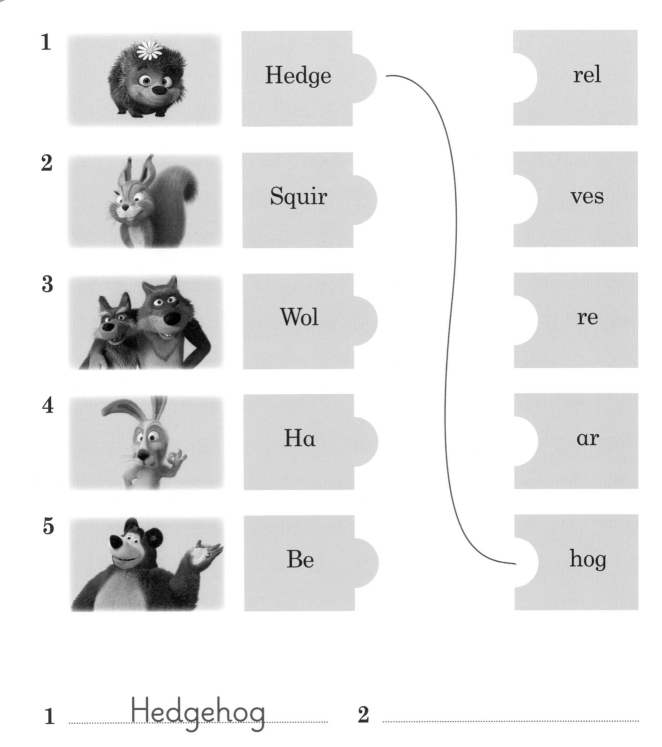

1 | Hedge | rel
2 | Squir | ves
3 | Wol | re
4 | Ha | ar
5 | Be | hog

1 <u>Hedgehog</u> 2 ....

3 .... 4 ....

5 ....

11 Listen, and write the answers. *

1 What can you see in the picture? Bowls of .... porridge ....

2 How many are there? There are ....

3 Who is sitting under the tree? ....

4 Why are they there? Because they ate ....

5 Who did Masha give porridge to? ....
and the Wolves, too.

6 What's the matter with them? They are all .... !

*To complete this activity, listen to track 3 of the Reader audio download available at **www.ladybirdeducation.co.uk**

12 Draw a picture of Masha. Read the questions and write about Masha. 📖 ✏️ ❓

1 What's your name?

My name is Masha.

2 What do you want to eat?

3 How do you make it?

4 Who do you want to eat it with?

13 Talk about the picture with a friend. Use *There is, There isn't, There are,* and *There aren't.*

1 **There is** a girl sitting in the kitchen.

2 . . . two books on the chair.

3 . . . any porridge in the bowl.

4 . . . any animals in the room.

14 Look at the pictures. Which picture is different? Put a ✓ in the correct boxes and write the sentences below. 📖 ✏️ ❓

> She is hungry.   There are two of them.
> It is clean.   He is coming home.

1

 a ✓

 b ☐

 c ☐

She is hungry.

2

 a ☐

 b ☐

 c ☐

3

 a ☐

 b ☐

 c ☐

4

 a ☐

 b ☐

 c ☐

15 Sing the song. *

Masha cleaned Bear's kitchen, and then
Bear's kitchen was clean again.
Masha put porridge in every bowl.
She gave some porridge to Squirrel.

Too much porridge in the pot.
Look, look how much porridge we've got!

Pink porridge, oh wow!
Masha gave some to Hare. He was very fat now.
Hedgehog, Wolves, what about you?
They ate lots of porridge and were very fat, too.

Too much porridge in the pot.
Look, look how much porridge we've got!

Lots of porridge! Bear was angry.
Masha said, "Bear, I'm tired and hungry."
Lots of oats, and milk, and jam.
Eat more porridge if you can!

Too much porridge in the pot.
Look, look how much porridge we've got!
Too much porridge in the pot.
Pink, pink porridge, lots and lots.

*To complete this activity, listen to track 4 of the Reader audio download available at www.ladybirdeducation.co.uk